THIS MINIONS 2 ANNUAL BELONGS TO:

....

I AM ....*9*........ YEARS OLD

MY FAVOURITE MINION IS:

Otto

....

ORCHARD BOOKS

First published in Great Britain in 2022 by The Watts Publishing Group

Minions: Rise of Gru © 2022 Universal City Studios LLC.
All Rights Reserved.

A CIP catalogue record for this book is available from the British Library

ISBN 978 1 40836 103 0

1 3 5 7 9 10 8 6 4 2

Printed and bound in China

Orchard Books
An imprint of Hachette Children's Group
Part of The Watts Publishing Group Limited Carmelite House
50 Victoria Embankment
London EC4Y 0DZ
An Hachette UK Company
www.hachette.co.uk
www.hachettechildrens.co.uk

Adult supervision is recommended when glue, paint, scissors or other sharp points are in use.

ILLUMINATION PRESENTS

minions 2

THE RISE OF GRU

ANNUAL 2023

CONTENTS

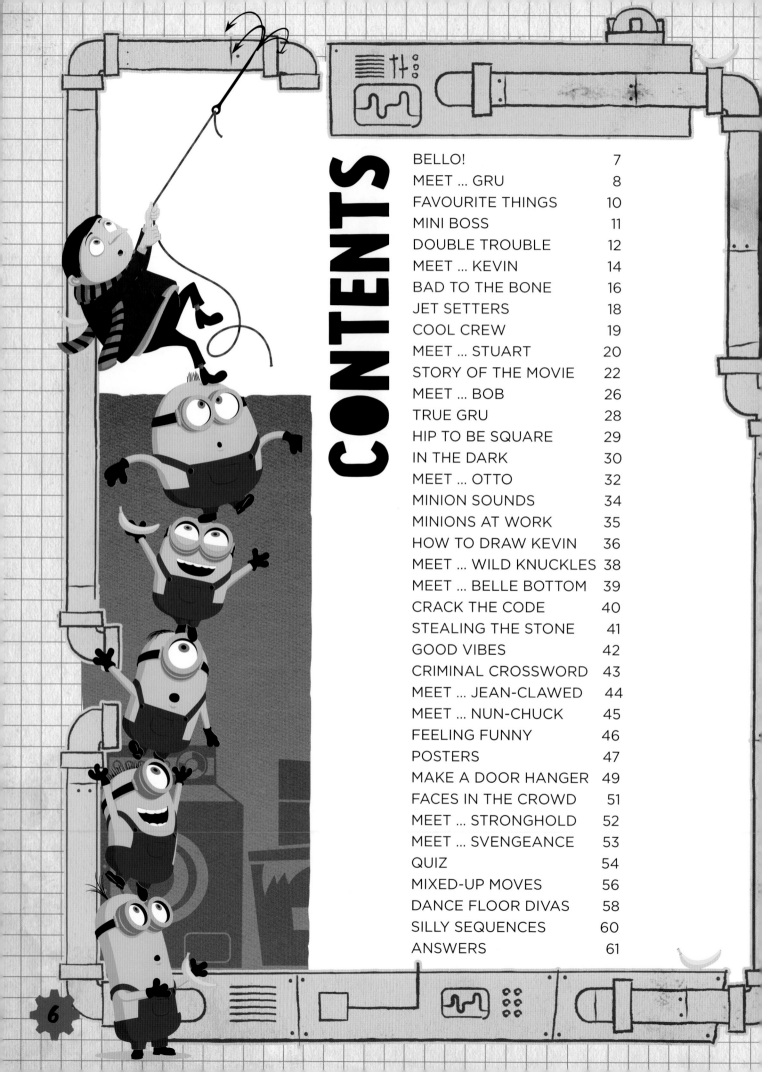

BELLO!

Kevin, Stuart and Bob first came face to face with a young Gru in London town. The Minions marvelled at the mini criminal's shameless swiping of the Queen's crown from under the noses of supervillains Scarlet and Herb Overkill. Still just a boy, Gru had proved he was already an evil genius – the Minions had at last found a worthy master to serve! Together they would be ...

UNSTOPPABLE!

SPOT SIX BANANAS HIDDEN ON THIS SPREAD.

MEET ... GRU

CAN YOU DO A SUPERVILLAIN STANCE LIKE GRU? STAND TALL WITH YOUR HANDS BEHIND YOUR BACK AND LOOK SMUG.

GRU ISN'T LIKE THE OTHER KIDS IN HIS NEIGHBOURHOOD (OR IN ANY OTHER NEIGHBOURHOOD, FOR THAT MATTER). DESPERATE TO BECOME A SUPERVILLAIN FROM A YOUNG AGE, HE'LL STOP AT NOTHING TO ACHIEVE HIS DEVIOUS DREAM. GRU APPLIES FOR A PLACE IN THE FEARSOME CRIMINAL GANG, THE VICIOUS 6, BUT THE INTERVIEW TAKES AN INTERESTING TURN ...

WANTED

FULL NAME: Felonius Gru

APPEARANCE: Small and menacing

CHARACTER TRAITS: Driven by despicable deeds, cunning

GETAWAY VEHICLE: A motorbike that transforms into an awesome Jet Bike

ADD SOME COLOUR TO GRU'S MUGSHOT.

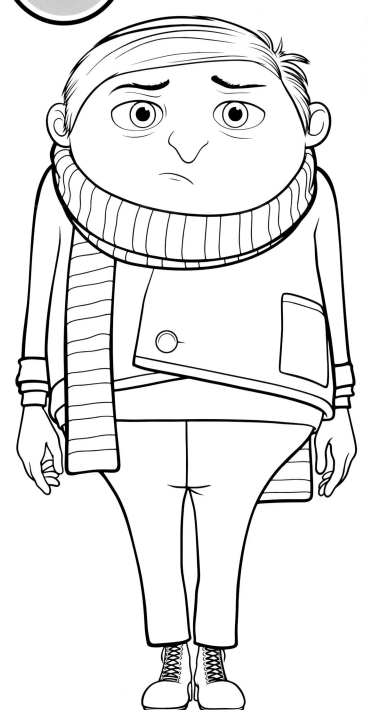

MEMORABLE MOMENTS

1

Using a Fart Grenade to clear a whole cinema, so he and his Minions could enjoy a private movie viewing.

2

Saving Wild Knuckles from a sticky end in his own pool of hungry crocodiles.

3

Stealing a priceless painting from the heavily guarded Bank of Evil.

FAVOURITE THINGS

The Minions are all in a tangle and have lost their prized possessions!
Follow the lines to see which item belongs to each Minion.

Answers on page 61.

MINI BOSS

Hands up if you love being bad!
Join the dots to reveal the
Minions' brand-new master.

NOW COLOUR IN THIS DASTARDLY VILLAIN.

DOUBLE TROUBLE

Trouble follows Gru wherever he goes!

LOOK CAREFULLY AT THE TWO SCENES AND TRY TO SPOT FIVE DIFFERENCES BETWEEN THEM.

COLOUR IN A BANANA FOR EACH DIFFERENCE YOU FIND.

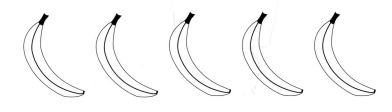

MEET... KEVIN

CAN YOU TRY KUNG FU MOVES AT HOME?

THE LEADER OF THE MINIONS, KEVIN IS A LOYAL SERVANT TO HIS MINI BOSS, GRU. HE LOVES TO SPEND TIME WITH HIS BEST BUDDIES, AND FORMS A TERRIBLE TRIO WITH STUART AND BOB. HIS NEXT CHALLENGE IS TO MASTER THE KUNG FU MOVES TAUGHT TO HIM BY MASTER CHOW.

WANTED

FULL NAME: Kevin the Minion

APPEARANCE: Tall and yellow

CHARACTER TRAITS: Bossy, determined, loyal

ADD SOME COLOUR TO KEVIN'S MUGSHOT.

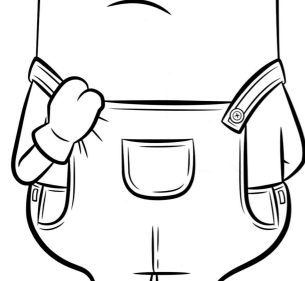

MEMORABLE MOMENTS

1
Expertly slam-dunking some basketballs at the arcade.

2
Mastering some tricky kung fu moves.

3
Captaining a jumbo jet with Stuart as his clueless co-pilot.

BAD TO THE BONE

The names of the baddest villains in town are hiding out in the grid on the next page. How many can you track down? The names read forwards, backwards, up, down and diagonally.

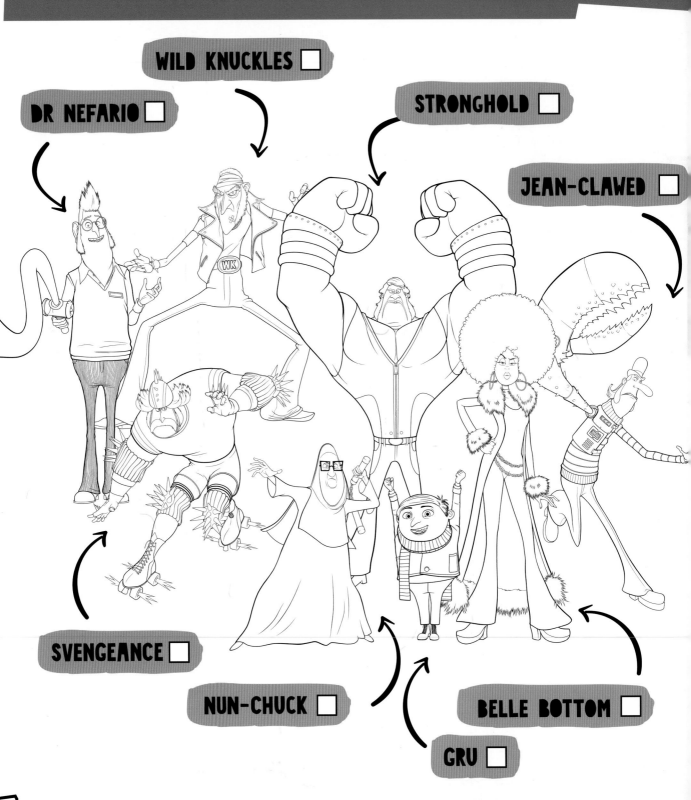

WILD KNUCKLES ☐

DR NEFARIO ☐

STRONGHOLD ☐

JEAN-CLAWED ☐

SVENGEANCE ☐

NUN-CHUCK ☐

BELLE BOTTOM ☐

GRU ☐

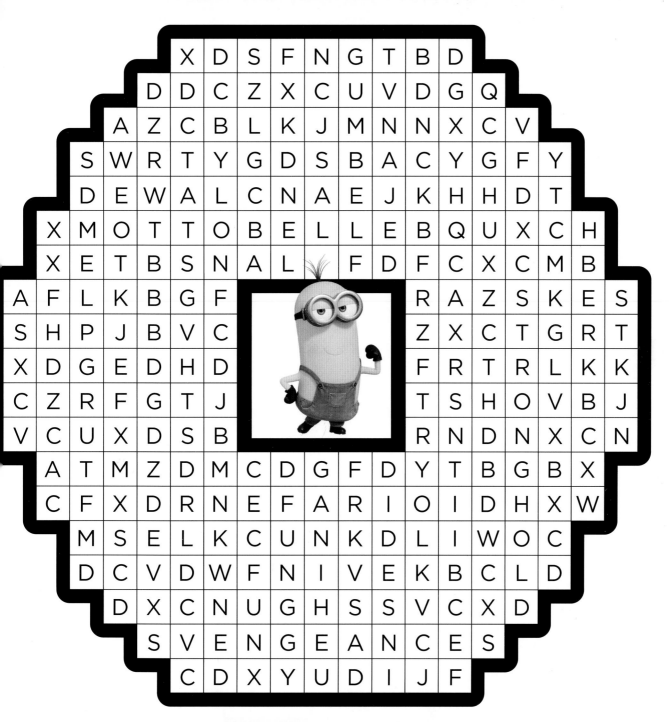

	X	D	S	F	N	G	T	B	D	
	D	D	C	Z	X	C	U	V	D	G	Q
	A	Z	C	B	L	K	J	M	N	N	X	C	V
S	W	R	T	Y	G	D	S	B	A	C	Y	G	F	Y
D	E	W	A	L	C	N	A	E	J	K	H	H	D	T
X	M	O	T	T	O	B	E	L	L	E	B	Q	U	X	C	H
X	E	T	B	S	N	A	L			F	D	F	C	X	C	M	B
A	F	L	K	B	G	F				R	A	Z	S	K	E	S
S	H	P	J	B	V	C				Z	X	C	T	G	R	T
X	D	G	E	D	H	D				F	R	T	R	L	K	K
C	Z	R	F	G	T	J				T	S	H	O	V	B	J
V	C	U	X	D	S	B				R	N	D	N	X	C	N
A	T	M	Z	D	M	C	D	G	F	D	Y	T	B	G	B	X
C	F	X	D	R	N	E	F	A	R	I	O	I	D	H	X	W
M	S	E	L	K	C	U	N	K	D	L	I	W	O	C
D	C	V	D	W	F	N	I	V	E	K	B	C	L	D
D	X	C	N	U	G	H	S	S	V	C	X	D
S	V	E	N	G	E	A	N	C	E	S
C	D	X	Y	U	D	I	J	F

MINION IN THE MIDDLE

Which Minion is pictured in the centre of the grid? Find his name too!

::

JET SETTERS

Bello! This is your captain speaking! Buckle up, then guide the Minion Air plane safely through the clouds to San Francisco Airport. Watch out for any other aircraft in your flight path!

Answers on page 61.

COOL CREW

Stuart and Kevin are pilots in training! Colour in the crew, using the little picture as a guide.

19

MEET... STUART

STUART LOVES DRESSING UP. WHAT'S YOUR FAVOURITE DRESSING UP OUTFIT?

SMOOTH-TALKING STUART IS THE ONE-EYED REBEL OF THE GROUP. STUART IS A NATURAL AT KUNG FU BUT MUST REMEMBER TO CONCENTRATE. WHEN HE'S NOT SERVING HIS MINI BOSS, STUART LOVES TO PRACTISE HIS LATEST KUNG FU MOVES!

WANTED

FULL NAME: Stuart the Minion

APPEARANCE: One eye, centre parting

CHARACTER TRAITS: Cool, excellent kung fu skills

ADD SOME COLOUR TO STUART'S MUGSHOT.

MEMORABLE MOMENTS

1
Dressing up as a pilot to stow away on board an aeroplane.

2
When he accidentally loses his clothes in the aeroplane toilet!

3
Disguising himself as a brick wall to fool Wild Knuckles' henchmen.

STORY OF THE MOVIE

When a young Gru foiled a plot to steal the Queen of England's crown, the Minions knew that they had found their most despicable master yet. Since that day, the Minions and their Mini Boss had been causing mayhem of the most evil kind!

It was the **BIGGEST DAY OF GRU'S LIFE**. He was on his way to meet **THE VICIOUS 6**, the baddest criminal gang in town. This bunch of supervillains were looking for a new recruit and Gru had applied for the position. Did he have what it takes to join the big league? He was about to find out.

Gru decided to go to his interview alone. But **KEVIN**, **STUART**, **BOB** and **OTTO**, his faithful Minions, followed in the shadows.

Gru approached the meeting venue, a shop called Criminal Records.

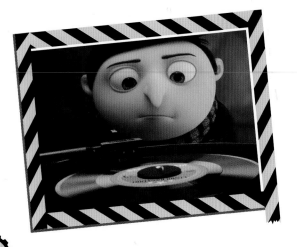

As he stepped inside, the man behind the counter greeted Gru with a big green wave. His name was Dr Nefario and the Sticky Hand was his latest invention!

"TAKE THIS," said the man mysteriously. **"YOU NEVER KNOW WHEN YOU MIGHT NEED A HELPING HAND."**

Gru shrugged and accepted the gift, before being quickly ushered into a listening booth. He placed a record on the record player, then spun it backwards to hear the message.

"WELCOME TO THE VICIOUS 6!" the record screeched.

The booth instantly transformed into a lift, plunging Gru deep underground towards the criminals' lair.

Gru took his seat among a **GANG OF HORRID HOPEFULS**, but he didn't have long to wait.

Now was his moment to shine!

He entered a large chamber and came face to face with **FIVE FEARSOME VILLAINS.** Leading the interviews for a sixth spot on the team was Belle Bottom.

"You seriously think that a puny child can be a villain?" she scoffed, when she saw Gru. "Come back when you've done something evil enough to impress me!" Her team of henchmen fell about laughing. Gru sighed.

"I'm pretty despicable," he warned Belle. "You don't want to cross me."

Gru was true to his word. When the villains' backs were turned, he aimed the Sticky Hand towards a glistening jewel on the chamber wall and fired. **BULLSEYE!** The hand sprung back and Gru pocketed the Stone, before making a swift exit. The clever kid had stolen the **LEGENDARY ZODIAC STONE** – the Vicious 6's most prized plunder – from under their very noses! Things were about to get serious ...

In the street, Gru and the Minions jumped onto Gru's Jet Bike. The Vicious 6 chased after them. When the bike skidded around a corner, Otto bounced off and the Stone went with him.

"TAKE THE STONE BACK TO THE LAIR," Gru ordered.

Luckily, the supervillains followed Gru instead of Otto! The villain pressed a button and his Jet Bike left the Vicious 6 for dust.

STORY OF THE MOVIE

Back in his lair, Gru was celebrating his most **DESPICABLE CRIME YET.**

"This kid just stole something from the worst villains in the world!" he boasted.

"Yaaay!" the Minions cheered and whooped.

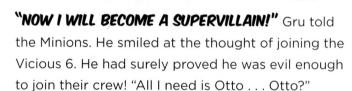

"NOW I WILL BECOME A SUPERVILLAIN!" Gru told the Minions. He smiled at the thought of joining the Vicious 6. He had surely proved he was evil enough to join their crew! "All I need is Otto . . . Otto?"

The Minion appeared and began rummaging in his dungarees. Seconds later, Otto pulled out a stone. "Ta-da!"

But to Gru's horror, it looked very different from the ancient Zodiac Stone! Otto, who was about as bright as a banana, had traded the precious jewel for a rock with googly eyes at a birthday party, while on his way home!

Gru had never been more furious!
"DID YOU JUST TRADE MY FUTURE FOR A PET ROCK?"
he boomed.

It was clear to Gru that the Minions weren't ready to mix with the big league. "You're all FIRED!" he screamed.

Determined to recover the Stone on his own, Gru packed up his things and left the house moments later.

LITTLE DID HE KNOW OF THE DANGER THAT LURKED JUST BEYOND HIS DOORSTEP ...

MEET... BOB

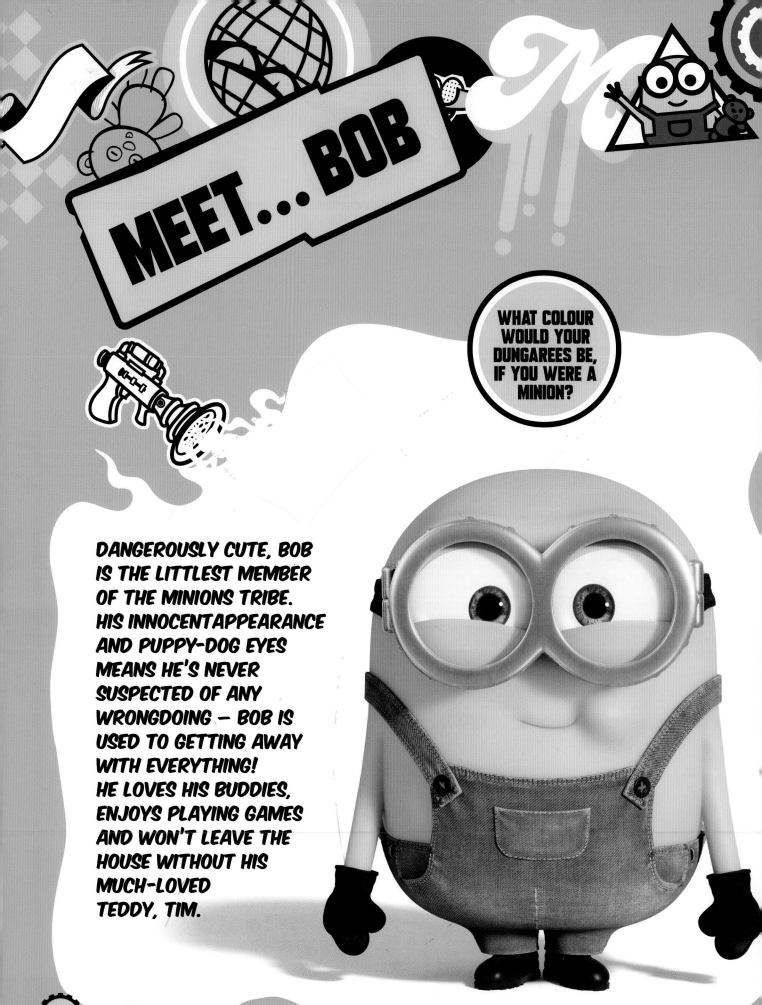

WHAT COLOUR WOULD YOUR DUNGAREES BE, IF YOU WERE A MINION?

DANGEROUSLY CUTE, BOB IS THE LITTLEST MEMBER OF THE MINIONS TRIBE. HIS INNOCENTAPPEARANCE AND PUPPY-DOG EYES MEANS HE'S NEVER SUSPECTED OF ANY WRONGDOING — BOB IS USED TO GETTING AWAY WITH EVERYTHING! HE LOVES HIS BUDDIES, ENJOYS PLAYING GAMES AND WON'T LEAVE THE HOUSE WITHOUT HIS MUCH-LOVED TEDDY, TIM.

WANTED

FULL NAME: Bob the Minion

APPEARANCE: Small and charming

CHARACTER TRAITS: Overly excitable, sweet and loyal

MEMORABLE MOMENTS

1
Snuggling up in bed with Gru after waking from a nightmare.

2
Becoming a sketch artist for Otto's interrogation.

3
Dressing up as a flight attendant on a Minions Air flight.

ADD SOME COLOUR TO BOB'S MUGSHOT.

TRUE GRU

Six young villains are plotting their next move, but only one is the true Gru! Circle the real Gru and cross out the imposters.

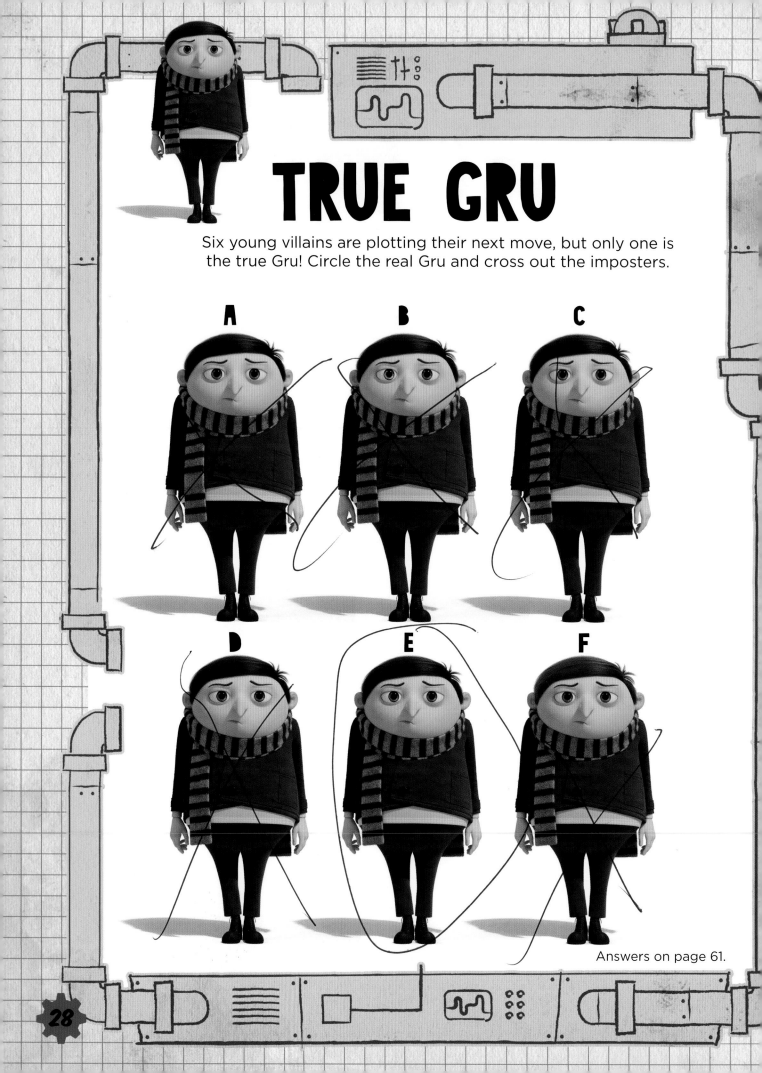

A

B

C

D

E

F

Answers on page 61.

HIP TO BE SQUARE

Join the dots to become the Minions' brand-new master.

INSTRUCTIONS

1 Play against a friend, taking turns to join two dots with a straight line (no diagonals).

2 If the line you draw completes a box, write your initials inside it and take another turn.

3 Score one point for each box containing your initials.

4 If a box you completed also contains a Minion, claim two points.

5 The winner is the player with the most points, once all the boxes have been completed.

KEEP A RECORD OF YOUR SCORES!

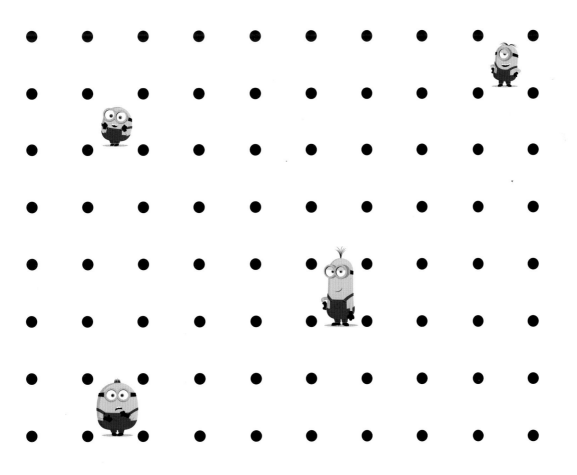

IN THE DARK

The Minions are exploring their Mini Boss's lair, but someone has turned out the lights! Unscramble the names, then write the correct name next to each of the shadows.

C

A

....

....

D

E

....

....

1. TRASTU   2. NIVEK   3. TOOT

4. OBB   5. VEDA   6. HIPL   7. LARC

B

....

F

....

G

....

Answers on page 61.

31

MEET... OTTO

OTTO LOVES HIS PET ROCK. WHAT WOULD YOUR PERFECT PET BE?

WHEN OTTO TRADES THE PRECIOUS ZODIAC STONE FOR A PET ROCK WITH GOOGLY EYES, HE REALISES HE HAS SOME MAKING UP TO DO. SO HE SETS OFF ON A QUEST ACROSS THE DESERT TO CHASE DOWN WHOEVER HAS THE STONE. OTTO WILL CHAT TO ANYONE WHO'LL LISTEN, BUT DOESN'T KNOW WHEN TO STOP TALKING!

WANTED

FULL NAME: Otto the Minion

APPEARANCE: Short with a neat haircut, wears braces

CHARACTER TRAITS: Easily distracted, never stops talking!

MEMORABLE MOMENTS

1
Otto's epic journey across the desert to reclaim the Zodiac Stone.

2
When Gru plays the 'quiet game' with Otto, so he can get a minute's peace!

3
Riding a dragon puppet through San Francisco's Chinatown.

ADD SOME COLOUR TO OTTO'S MUGSHOT.

MINION SOUNDS

Do you speak Minionese? Decide which of the words below are Minion words. Make your way from start to finish, making a path of Minionese words.

START

LAGOON   FIZZLE   DONGLE   BELLO

INKLING   COMPAI   BLUMOCK   GIZMO

POOPAYE   GROMMET   BEANPOLE   PIFFLE

QUIBBLE   BAPPLES   POGO   CLAPTRAP

FINISH

Answers on page 61.

MINIONS AT WORK

The Minions are hard at work building a lair fit for a master criminal, their Mini Boss, Gru! Colour in the picture to complete the busy basement scene.

HOW TO DRAW KEVIN

The tallest of the tribe, Kevin is the Minions' lovable leader.
Follow the steps below to perfectly draw his portrait!

1 Start by drawing a long sausage shape using a pencil.

2 Next, about two-thirds of the way down his body, sketch out triangles for Kevin's arms and circles for hands.

5 The next step is to draw Kevin's shoes.

6 Add the final details, such as buttons, a dungaree pocket and sprig of hair.

 3 Draw Kevin's dungarees, starting with the straps.

4 Now draw two connected circles with outlines for Kevin's goggles and add the strap on the right.

7 Now you try!

NOW ADD SOME COLOUR TO KEVIN!

KEVIN

MEET... WILD KNUCKLES

APPEARANCE: Skinny with sideburns

CHARACTER TRAITS: Smart and sneaky, trust him at your peril!

GETAWAY VEHICLE: He drives an orange and black van

THE FOUNDER OF THE VICIOUS 6, WILD KNUCKLES WAS ONCE THE WORLD'S GREATEST VILLAIN. HE KNOWS EVERY FIGHTING MOVE ON EARTH, FROM THE BELGIAN FIVE-ARMED NOSE PICK TO THE LITHUANIAN HAIRCUT. WHEN HIS CRIMINAL GANG BETRAYS HIM, WILD KNUCKLES FINDS AN UNLIKELY ALLY IN YOUNG GRU.

ADD SOME COLOUR TO WILD KNUCKLES'S MUGSHOT.

WANTED

MEET... BELLE BOTTOM

APPEARANCE: Big hair, big flares
CHARACTER TRAITS: Stylish and ruthless
GETAWAY VEHICLE: The Super Ship

ADD SOME COLOUR TO BELLE'S MUGSHOT.

DOUBLE-CROSSING BELLE BOTTOM HAS AMBITIONS TO TAKE OVER THE WORLD! WITH HER DASTARDLY COMPANIONS, SHE FORCES CURRENT BOSS WILD KNUCKLES INTO AN EARLY RETIREMENT. BELLE VALUES MONEY AND POWER OVER LOYALTY AND IS COMMITTED TO GETTING WHAT SHE WANTS. HER GROOVY CHAIN BELT TURNS INTO A LETHAL WEAPON.

CRACK THE CODE

A terrible crime has just been committed! What has been stolen and who is the thief? Use the key to crack the code and find out.

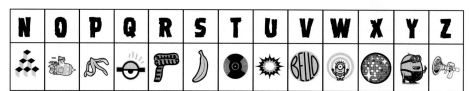

Wild knuckles

has stolen

the zodiac

stone

WARNING THIS MESSAGE WILL SELF-DESTRUCT IN 5 MINUTES!

Answers on page 61.

STEALING THE STONE

Wild Knuckles summons the rest of The Vicious 6, who arrive with rescue vehicle, the Super Ship. Little does he know that he's about to be double-crossed! Colour in the Super Ship and the gang of crooked criminals.

WHAT WOULD YOUR SUPERVILLAIN VEHICLE LOOK LIKE?

GOOD VIBES

Peace, love and Minions! Guide Bob through the maze to find Kevin. Which path will lead Bob to his buddy?

START

FINISH

42

The answers are on page

CRIMINAL CROSSWORD

With criminals like these on the loose, no one is safe! Read the clues to work out which vicious villains appear in the crossword.

The answers are on page 61.

DOWN

1. A baddie with an iron touch, his two fists are like wrecking balls.
2. This Swedish offender is a high-roller.
3. A villain whose chain belt turns into a mace.
7. A genius engineer with a passion for gadgets.

ACROSS

4. The feisty Frenchman has a powerful claw.
5. A boss who's betrayed by his cruel criminal crew.
6. A young villain with a natural talent for evil.
8. This sly criminal sure has a bad habit!

MEET... JEAN-CLAWED

WANTED

APPEARANCE: His right arm has been replaced by an enormous robotic claw

CHARACTER TRAITS: Stubborn and stone-faced

GETAWAY VEHICLE: The cool Claw-Mobile

OUTFITTED WITH A GIANT MECHANICAL LOBSTER CLAW, FRENCHMAN JEAN-CLAWED IS SERIOUS ABOUT BEING BAD. HE GETS SUPER-ANGRY WHEN HE LEARNS THAT GRU HAS STOLEN THE ZODIAC STONE AND VOWS TO TAKE HIS REVENGE ON THE YOUNG CRIMINAL — AT ANY COST.

ADD SOME COLOUR TO JEAN-CLAWED'S MUGSHOT.

WANTED

MEET... NUN-CHÜCK

APPEARANCE: Her full habit with a sad sandals-and-socks combo is not a good look!

CHARACTER TRAITS: Shameful and sly

GETAWAY VEHICLE: An Organ-Mobile that lurches into action when Nun-Chuck presses the organ chords!

ADD SOME COLOUR TO NUN-CHUCK'S MUGSHOT.

DON'T BE FOOLED BY NUN-CHUCK'S SAINTLY APPEARANCE; LURKING BENEATH HER HUMBLE HABIT IS A WILD WARRIOR WITH SOME SERIOUS MOVES. THIS NUN HAS BEEN ON THE RUN FROM THE LAW FOR YEARS, SAVED ONLY BY HER DASTARDLY DISGUISE. HER WEAPON OF CHOICE? HER PRIZED NUN-CHUCKS, OF COURSE!

FEELING FUNNY

Share these seriously silly jokes with your friends and family to make them laugh like a Minion!

Q: WHY DID THE MINION TAKES ITS BANANA TO THE DOCTORS?

A: It wasn't peeling very well!

Q: WHAT'S YELLOW AND WEARS SUNGLASSES?

A: A Minion on holiday.

Q: WHY DIDN'T THE TEDDY BEAR WANT PUDDING?

A: It was already stuffed!

Q: WHY DID THE MINIONS BRING THEIR MASTER TO THE DISCO?

A: Because he was the Gru-viest dancer in town.

Q: WHAT DO YOU CALL TWO BANANAS?

A: A pair of slippers.

MAKE A DOOR HANGER

Get crafty by making your own Minions door hanger – perfect for your own lair!

YOU WILL NEED:
- Scissors

HOW TO MAKE:

1 Carefully cut out the page along the vertical dotted line.

2 Now cut around the door hanger shape.

3 Choose which side to show on the door to your lair.

MAKE SURE YOU ASK A GROWN-UP BEFORE USING SCISSORS.

ENTER AT YOUR OWN RISK! KUNG FU CLASS IN PROGRESS!

MAKE A
DOOR HANGER

**MAKE SURE
YOU ASK A
GROWN-UP
BEFORE USING
SCISSORS.**

BELLO

**NO ENTRY!
VILLAINS
HATCHING
PLANS!**

FACES IN THE CROWD

Give your goggles a wipe, then look carefully to find each of the items on the list.

Answers on page 61.

MEET... STRONGHOLD

APPEARANCE: Oversized arms with iron gloves

CHARACTER TRAITS: Extreme strength

GETAWAY VEHICLE: An indestructible armoured tank

SERIOUSLY SOLID, STRONGHOLD IS THE BRAWN BEHIND THE VICIOUS 6. THIS HULK OF A VILLAIN HAS GIANT IRON HANDS THAT CAUSE HIS ENEMIES TO RUN A MILE BUT CAN MAKE SIMPLE TASKS LIKE HOLDING A GLASS OF WATER ALMOST IMPOSSIBLE!

ADD SOME COLOUR TO STRONGHOLD'S MUGSHOT.

WANTED

MEET... SVENGEANCE

APPEARANCE: Moustached and mighty

CHARACTER TRAITS: Super speedy

GETAWAY VEHICLE: The ultra slick Roller-Mobile

ADD SOME COLOUR TO SVENGEANCE'S MUGSHOT.

ATHLETIC SVENGEANCE IS A ROLLER-SKATING CHAMPION WHO HAILS FROM SWEDEN. A MASTER CRIMINAL ON WHEELS, HE SPEEDS AFTER HIS ENEMIES AND SENDS THEM PACKING WITH A SERIES OF POWERFUL SPIN KICKS USING HIS SPIKED SKATES.

ILLUMINATION PRESENTS

minions 2 QUIZ
THE RISE OF GRU

LOOK BACK THROUGH THE BOOK FOR CLUES!

Tackle the ten teasers in this tricky quiz to prove yourself as a mega Minions fan.

1. WHAT IS THE LEGENDARY TREASURE THAT WILD KNUCKLES PLANS TO STEAL?

A. The Queen's crown ☐

B. The Mona Lisa ☐

C. The Zodiac Stone ☑

2. WHAT JOB DOES A YOUNG GRU SAY HE WANTS TO DO WHEN HE GROWS UP?

A. Record shop owner ☐

B. Supervillain ☑

C. Astronaut ☐

3. DURING OTTO'S PEP TALK FOR THE VICIOUS 6 INTERVIEW, HOW DOES GRU GET HIM TO STOP TALKING?

A. Shoots him with a Fart Gun ☐

B. Offers him food ☐

C. Plays the Quiet Game ☑

4. WHICH CONTRAPTION DOES GRU USE TO STEAL THE ZODIAC STONE WHILE AT HIS VICIOUS 6 INTERVIEW?

A. The Sticky Hand ☑

B. A ray gun that fires cheese ☐

C. A Fart Blaster gun ☐

5. WHICH MINIONS DISGUISE THEMSELVES AS PILOTS TO FLY TO SAN FRANCISCO, IN SEARCH OF THEIR MISSING MASTER?

A. Otto and Stuart ☐

B. Kevin and Bob ☐

C. Kevin and Stuart ☑

6. WHAT DISGUISES DO WILD KNUCKLES AND GRU WEAR WHEN THEY ROB THE BANK OF EVIL?

A. Disco outfits and roller skates ☐

B. Grandpa and scout ☑

C. Santa Claus and elf ☐

7. WHAT IS OCCUPYING THE POOL AT WILD KNUCKLES' HEADQUARTERS?

A. A bask of crocodiles ☑

B. A family of inflatable flamingos ☐

C. A tribe of Minions ☐

9. GRU'S MUM IS HAVING A PARTY AND NEEDS THE MINIONS' HELP TO SELL...

A. Make-up ☐

B. Plastic storage boxes ☑

C. Homemade cookies ☐

8. HOW DOES OTTO HITCH A LIFT IN CHINATOWN?

A. On board the Vicious 6's Super Ship ☐

B. On the back of a dragon puppet ☑

C. In an armoured tank ☐

CHECK YOUR ANSWERS ON PAGE 61, THEN RECORD YOUR SCORE.

MY SCORE:

9

HOW DID YOU SCORE?

8-9
Compai! Super Minions knowledge!

6-7
Tank yu! A good effort.

4-5
Bi do! Try harder next time.

1-3
Blumock! An epic fail.

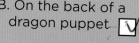

MIXED-UP MOVES

Kevin and his buddies are training to be kung fu masters but they keep mixing up their moves! Piece each Minion back together in the correct order to unleash their attacks.

OTTO

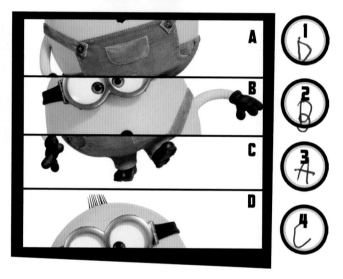

A
B
C
D

1 b
2 b
3 A
4 c

STUART

1 b
2 c
3 b
4 a

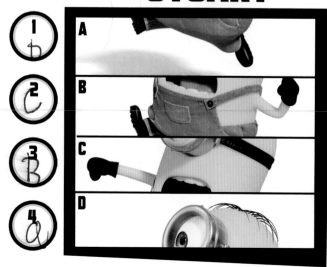

A
B
C
D

BOB

A
B
C
D

1 b
2 d
3 d
4 c

KEVIN

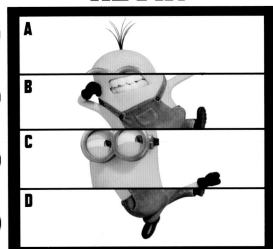

1. a
2. C
3. B
4. D

DAVE

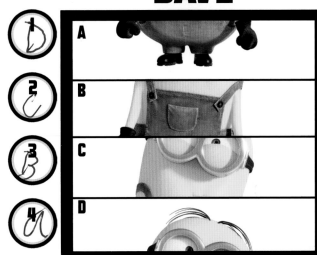

1. D
2. C
3. B
4. a

Answers on page 61.

DANCE FLOOR DIVAS

The Minions are on a mission and need your help! They must rescue their Mini Boss from Disco Inferno before Gru spins into serious trouble. Grab a dice, a friend or two and a counter for each player, and get ready to bust some move

START | **1** | **2**

3 You obey the call of the dance floor! Move forwards three spaces.

7 Stuart rolls over your toes. Go back to the start.

4 | **5** | **6**

27 | **26**

25 Stop for a snack. Miss a turn.

24 | **23**

28

29 You're feeling the beat! Take another turn.

30 | **31** | **32**

58

HOW TO PLAY:

1. The youngest player goes first.
2. Take it in turns to throw the dice and move around the board.
3. If you land on a space with text, follow the instructions.
4. If you land on a BANANA space, take an extra turn.
5. The first player to reach the FINISH is the winner.

9

10

11

12

13
Trouble on the dance floor! Miss a turn.

14

15

16
You're looking sharp. Dance forwards two spaces.

17

18

17
Bob has lost Tim! Move back four spaces to find him.

20

21

22
Slide on your knees. Move forwards one space.

33
The music stops! Throw a six to move on.

34

35

FINISH

59

SILLY SEQUENCES

Blumock! Some of the pictures from these patterns have disappeared. Draw the missing pictures in each row.

1

2

3

4

5

Answers on page 61.

ANSWERS

PAGE 10

PAGE 28

GRU E IS THE REAL VILLAIN

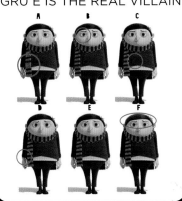

PAGE 13

PAGE 17

MIDDLE MINION IS KEVIN

PAGE 18

PAGE 31

MINION NAMES:

1. STUART
2. KEVIN
3. OTTO
4. BOB
5. DAVE
6. PHIL
7. CARL

MINION SHADOWS:

A. CARL
B. DAVE
C. OTTO
D. BOB
E. KEVIN
F. STUART
G. PHIL

PAGE 34

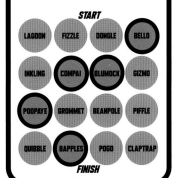

PAGE 40

The message reads:
WILD KNUCKLES
HAS STOLEN THE
ZODIAC STONE.

PAGE 42

PAGE 43

PAGE 51

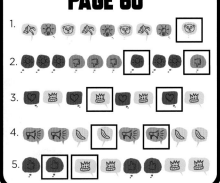

PAGES 54-55

1.C 2.B 3.C 4.A 5.C
6.B 7.B 8.A 9.B

PAGES 56-57

OTTO: 1-D 2-B 3-A 4-C
STUART: 1-D 2-C 3-B 4-A
BOB: 1-B 2-A 3-D 4-C
KEVIN: 1-A 2-C 3-B 4-D
DAVE: 1-D 2-C 3-B 4-A

PAGE 60

1.
2.
3.
4.
5.